THE Color OF CARE

A Beginner's Guide for the African American Caregiver

Ky'a Jackson

Edited by Zawn Villines

Interior and exterior design by Emmanuel Sofolawe

Adinkra Symbol definitions from http://www.adinkra.org

Table of Contents

Introduction

I became a caregiver at the age of 14. It was a huge job to take on, but I did it knowing in my heart that it was the right thing to do. During the most stressful moments, God and I would have many conversations about whether or not I was the right person to do the job and why he would have given such a heavy cross to bear to a person so young. Each time there was an obstacle or setback, God would give me the strength, patience, and encouragement to go on for another day.

My job as caregiver to my mother, Antoinette Jackson, ended on September 23, 2006. She passed away from complications due to Multiple Sclerosis. She was a soldier, I tell you, and to this day I am amazed at how she managed to sustain her positive outlook, faith, and sense of humor through all of her physical and emotional pain. I went through a few of the "normal" reactions you go through when a loved one passes away, but what's more interesting is that I went through a "peaceful" phase. I know it sounds strange, but I had an overall sense of calm that I am not sure everyone goes through during grief. Then I remembered something that my mother told me about many years earlier in my childhood. She said, "When you do what you are supposed to do and you are good to your parents, the grieving is different."

My mother always believed in helping people. She would take the clothes off her back; she would give her last dime to anyone who needed it. I remember once someone asked her if she had any sugar they could borrow. My mother had just bought a five-pound bag and without hesitation, offered them more than half of her bag of sugar. As a child, I didn't understand her desire, her need, to give so much to so many. Most of them would never even know that it was indeed her who had helped them, but as I grew older and continued to watch her, I understood.

with all the extra time I had in my days. My brother said I should fill this time focusing on something that is "worth it." With that advice, I began to write. Everyone grieves differently, and for an entire year I wrote through my grief and tears as I remembered the lessons, hardships, and even funny stories from my life as a caregiver. It hurt like crazy to remember but I knew I had to push through it.

This book is the physical manifestation of my grief mixed with the joy of my memories. My mother's life is its inspiration. Throughout this book I will tell you of my personal experiences as a caregiver of color. It is through that lens I will offer you advice, encouragement, and references, to help you become the best caregiver you can be. Some things you read you may not agree with or may have already resolved in your new role as a caregiver. Some things you may wave your hands in the air to proclaim, "Amen! That's right!" I encourage you to take plenty of notes and keep an open mind.

The most important thing I want you to know is that you are not alone in this journey of caregiving. As African Americans, we often do not want to let others know we need help, or even that we are afraid. My prayer is that when you use this guide, you will feel stronger and smarter, so when you have to handle any one of your caregiving tasks, you can do it armed with all the tools that will make you the best possible caregiver. Let's go through this journey together. Are you ready?

Ky'a

Special Acknowledgments

When others just did their jobs, you went over and beyond what you were paid to do. Without you, it would not have been possible for me to get my mother the best care she needed and deserved. I will forever thank you all for caring for my mother as you would care for your own.

Dr. Paul Schraeder
Dr. Jay E. DeMesquita
Mr. Ralph Robinson, Sr.
Dr. David Tabby
NMSS- Greater Delaware Valley
Multiple Sclerosis Association of America
Ms. Gwendolyn Partlowe
Ms. Lois Gardner
Dr. Richard Levine
Lankenau Hospital (4th Floor) Staff
Ms. Marie Hamm
Ms. Charlotte Jackson
Rev. Patricia Mann

Dedication

This book is dedicated to my mother, Antoinette B. Jackson - a woman who had the strength of a warrior, a heart of gold and the faith of Job.

Part

1

YOU ARE THE CHOSEN ONE

BOA ME NA ME MMOA WO
"Help me and let me help you"
symbol of cooperation and interdependence

Congratulations! You have just been given the daunting yet rewarding task of being the primary caregiver for your loved one. You're not quite sure how you got the position. There was no interview process. No other applicants. No trial period where you could ask yourself, "Can I do this?" and feel comfortable with your answer. Maybe you volunteered. Maybe you got the job by default. It doesn't matter whether you wanted it or not. I am sorry. It doesn't really work that way. Here you are.

You might find yourself wondering if someone else is better qualified to do this difficult job. The answer is simple — no. The questions in your mind then hit you like an avalanche: How do I do this? Will someone help me? How much money is this going to cost me? Will people think badly of me if I don't do this right? Most of these questions are fair to ask, and surprisingly easy to answer.

The question at the top of your list, however, is more important and more fundamental: why me? There were probably other siblings, aunts, uncles, cousins, the next-door neighbor, that could have been given this job. Your loved one chose to trust you. They chose you to be their voice. They chose you from every person they know or knew to help them through what is probably their toughest fight ever. You may never get the answer to the "why me?" question, because the person you are caring for may not be able to explain it in words. They just know in their hearts whom they want to be their advocate. Whether it's cancer, Multiple Sclerosis, diabetes, or any other serious health issue, you are the chosen one. I know you probably don't feel like it now, but this is a position of honor.

This is not to imply that this isn't going to be one of the biggest responsibilities of your life. This is one tough job. But remembering the role of the chosen one will help you during times when you feel like giving up. If you are a parent, becoming a caregiver for a loved one may not be that much of a transition. You are already used to sacrificing tremendous amounts of time and energy to take care of someone. But there are many of you who may be putting on the caregiver shoes for the first time and let me tell you, those new shoes are going to pinch something fierce! But just like any pair of new shoes, the longer you wear them, the more comfortable they become.

Being a caregiver is a role that is going to require you to exert a lot of emotional, mental, and physical energy. You will have to reach deep down into areas of your soul that may feel foreign and uncomfortable. It will require you to view people and situations very differently than you once did. I'll give you an example. Right now you're thinking, "I don't know if I can do this" or perhaps "Man, this is going to be a lot of work for me".

Now, imagine yourself in your loved one's shoes. Imagine that you were the one with diabetes, or MS, or the one with kidney failure who has to go through dialysis three to four times a week. Not so fun, right? Just remember, when you are done running errands for your loved one, you get to go back home and go about your daily routine. They are still stuck with what ails them. This new perspective is difficult for some adults to learn quickly so if you are a teenage caregiver, as I was, please be patient with yourself. Now that I think about it, all of you reading this guide – regardless of your age - should be patient with yourselves! Rome wasn't built in a day, you know! Everything worth anything takes time, so take the time you need to read, learn, and observe.

You have this new title now, but you may not know what it means or what to do. You want to know how to prepare. You want to know how long you will have to do this. Slow down. Breathe. No, really. I am serious. Count to two while you inhale and again while you exhale. You would be amazed at how much this small action will help you. Try it now before reading the next paragraph.

Ok, now isn't that a little better? Good. One of the most important things you will learn as a caregiver is that you can only handle one thing at a time. There is always going to be something that needs to be done. It can and will be overwhelming. You can't be perfect. No one expects you to know everything all the time. You will make mistakes. But remember, no one is keeping score here. And if there are people around you that are keeping score and only telling you all the things you are not doing right; you need to separate yourself from them and surround yourself with positive people (We'll save conversations about this for an upcoming chapter). All anyone should expect from you is for you to do and be the best person and the best caregiver you can be. Whether you were asked to be a caregiver or if you were thrust into the role by default, you and your loved one are now a team. Those closest to you are part of your team, too. You will care for your loved one and your team will help care for you.

I will be honest with you: it takes very special people to be part of your team. Some friends and/or family members may not be up to the challenge of being there for you when you need them. They may say some things that are just plain ole hurtful, whether they mean to or not. They may not be able to understand your new role and what responsibilities being the chosen one carries. I learned this the hard way when a close friend of my mother's abruptly stopped hanging out with her when my mother had to use a cane. I found out years later that my mom's friend just had a hard time seeing my mother's health deteriorate and felt she needed to separate herself. If something like this has happened to you already, do not hold ill feelings. I didn't. If people change how they interact with you because of your new role, it doesn't necessarily make them bad people. It just makes them human. The good thing is that you will find sources of strength and support from people that you least expect. So keep your eyes open and when you find those people, add them to your team. Make sure you let them know how much you appreciate them. Never, ever take them for granted.

There is so much to learn as the chosen one. Be patient, learn as much as you can, and always remember, this road you are about to take with your loved one is not about you. I am not saying that you are not an important factor in this journey. But the real journey here is your loved ones to take. As I said, you will need to think differently. Putting yourself in your loved one's shoes is a necessity to learning and adjusting. Most people do not know how to do this. If you are one of those people, you must learn it quickly because your loved one is trusting and relying on you. There is little to no learning curve here. I am not trying to scare you; I am trying to inform you. The positivity you gain from this experience will more than likely be the positivity you bring to this experience. When it's all said and done, if you put your all into it, you will be able to walk away comfortably knowing that you gave this job 150% of your effort. And believe me, there is nothing better than that.

So, where do we begin? You have just been informed that you will need to be a caregiver. Either you and your loved one came to this decision together, or you have just received information from a health care professional about your loved one's health status. My title of chosen one came when my brother, mother, and I were at a routine eye doctor visit. My mother had been complaining about her eyesight being blurry for quite some time. When she told our eye doctor this, he took a look in her eyes and noticed something strange. My brother and I knew something was wrong but didn't know what was happening to our mother. Whatever it was that the optometrist saw made him ask a series of specific questions, and then he suggested to my mother that she see a neurologist. My mother took his advice. At first, no one could find anything wrong. Her body, however, told a different story. She was getting fatigued rapidly. She struggled to see clearly and her speech was slurring. A woman who always loved walking, found herself falling even when she would stand still.

Many months and a few doctors later, we finally heard from the neurologist exactly what was going on. My mother had Multiple Sclerosis. The neurologist had given my brother and me our title of chosen one, and let me tell you, at 14 and 11 years old, my brother and

I had no idea what we were up against. We were woefully unprepared. Despite all we didn't know, what we did know is that we loved each other and that we could get through even the toughest roads ahead with our love, our humor and a strong belief that we could get through anything together.

Part 2 ASSEMBLING THE "DREAM TEAM"

FUNTUNFUNEFU-DENKYEMFUNEFU
"Siamese crocodiles"
symbol of democracy and unity

No matter what medical challenge your loved one faces, a good relationship with their doctors is key. If this is a new situation for you and your loved one, you will need to assemble a healthcare "Dream Team". This is the group of healthcare professionals that will work with you on the care of your loved one. The size of the team depends on the amount of care that your loved one needs. For example, my nephew, Xavier, has diabetes and he has a relatively small team. His dream team consists of an endocrinologist, podiatrist, dietician, RN, eye doctor, and primary care physician.

Having the right dream team isn't the only key to your loved one's care. You need to make sure that these qualified doctors will care for the person as well as the ailment. Let's face it, the healthcare industry has become more of a business and, in some cases, lost focus on what really matters – the people. On occasion, we have all felt the emotional detachment from nurses, doctors, etc. If you don't think this is true, simply view how surprised you are when you have the pleasure of getting a nice nurse on a hospital visit. You shouldn't be shocked by a caring medical professional. In my opinion, quality medical care and excellent medical customer service are not mutually exclusive. I am happy to say that I have had my share of nice nurses, doctors, and other healthcare professionals during the time I was caring for my mother, but I have also had my share of healthcare jerks.

Assembling the dream team will take a lot of homework. Do not just pick doctors based on loose criteria. For example, I have a family member that selected a doctor because my grandmother went to him and he was great for my grandmother so why wouldn't he be good for any other family member? Wrong! The criteria should be so much stricter than familiarity.

Look at their hospital affiliations. Check and see what schools they went to and what they specialize in. Even the smallest thing, like whether they speak another language, can make all the difference. The more you know about the doctor, the easier it will be for you to decide if you think that doctor will be a good fit for your loved one. There may be some of you who do not have the financial means or the best health insurance, and you may feel like getting the best doctors is not possible because of your situation. It may be more difficult to find a specialist (if one is needed) that is affordable. I was in that same boat myself, but I will tell you that it may be difficult to find a good doctor, but not impossible. When I tell you that you will need to do your homework, this is part of the homework as well. With a smartphone or computer at home (or in the library), your search becomes much easier.

A simple Internet search offers a lot of information, including reviews. Don't be afraid to research them online or call their offices and ask what type of health insurance they accept. Pay close attention to how you are treated when you call their office. This will give you a clear perspective on how you'll be treated after you actually become a patient. Most importantly, make sure that while you are getting information, you get the names of the people with whom you speak. You never want to forget the people who were not helpful in case you need to report them to their supervisor, and you want to keep the names of the people who helped you just in case you need their help again.

After you have done your homework on the doctors that you need, set up an initial meeting or conference call with them to discuss your loved ones needs. I observe everything when it comes to picking a doctor. Even for myself. When I call a doctor's office, I am not just trying to set up an appointment, but I am also observing how the doctor's office runs and how the staff treats its patients. There have been a few doctors that I did not choose for my mother based on something as simple as the office manager being rude or impatient on the phone during my initial phone call. Let's face it, if they were rude to me when I was just asking questions, then I certainly didn't want them dealing with my mother!

Remember to gather all the paperwork necessary for your doctor search. HIPAA, although it was created to protect the privacy of people's health information, can also be a hassle. You may need a power of attorney, and you'll likely need to show this to all your loved one's healthcare providers. Some medical providers may also require your loved one to sign an authorization. Do this at your first appointment to avoid any future delays and disputes.

Always bring an extra copy of important paperwork, such as the healthcare power of attorney, with you so that if you are ever questioned, you will be prepared. And believe me, every time you accompany your loved one to the doctor or have to handle medical business, you will be asked if you have permission to access their records.

Once you have established that the doctor you have chosen is good for your loved one, then schedule an appointment for your loved one to meet them as well. This is your loved one's life and body. They need and deserve to be involved. Remember it is not about you taking over their care; it is about you working with them in their care. Discuss with them what type of doctor they would like to have. In my case, all my mother's doctors had to have the ability to connect with their patients. My mother was not good at dealing with cookie cutter care. She wanted all of her doctors to care about her as a person, which for her meant that they had to know she was a strong believer in family, a strong desire to remain as independent as she could be and that she wasn't really a fan of taking medication.

Depending on what specific disability, ailment, or health issues your loved one has, you will need to make sure that you carefully choose all the members of the dream team. Once your team is chosen, it is up to you to facilitate communication between your loved one and all the "players" on the team. This can be difficult. Doctors of different specialties do not always share the same medical priorities. You may have to play mediator. For example, my mother had a lot of gastric issues with her Multiple Sclerosis. Of course, the obvious thing to do was to consult with her gastroenterologist; however, the gastroenterologist could not just view her as they would a regular

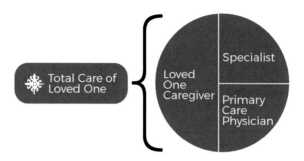

patient. The gastroenterologist had to consider that she had MS and speak to her neurologist, as well as her speech therapist in order to understand the interrelated causes of the problem.

So you see, the doctors must be able to connect with each other as well as your loved one. Each time one of the "players" in the team changes the "play," all the other teammates must be made aware of these changes. This may include changes in medication, allergies, their last cold or anything that affects the treatment plan.

If you are a fan of football, the primary care physician (PCP) is your loved one's team quarterback. Or in basketball he or she would be considered your loved one's team point guard. The PCP lays out all the plays for any other specialists your loved one will need.

The PCP and your loved one play on an equal field. No longer should there be the old school mentality that the doctor is more important than you or your loved one. or that whatever he or she says goes. Good doctors should be telling you the status of your loved one's care and providing you both with all the options you have in any given scenario. This empowers you and your loved one—the decision-makers, to make the best possible decisions. The doctor is not the decision-maker, even if he or she disapproves of your choices.

If your loved one is not in a position mentally or emotionally to be a part of the decision-making process, this leaves you to make these critical decisions. The PCP should always make sure that you have the information you need. Information is power. Yes, there will be doctors who still believe in that old "what I say goes" mentality, and they might even try to make you feel like your opinion doesn't matter, but it does.

Once you choose the PCP, you have opportunity to look for other doctors that will work him or her. Most PCPs will already have an idea of who your loved one should go to for other evaluations. Ask if you can have a list of those doctors so that you can do your own research. Remember, you are an important part of this process, and do have a say in who you want on your dream team. Communication is key here. Discuss with your doctor what you are looking for in a medical professional, and together you can get the best care for your loved one within whatever parameters you there are with your health insurance or lack thereof.

THE TOP TEN THINGS YOU SHOULD KNOW AS THE PRIMARY CAREGIVER

Part

3

NYANSAPO
"wisdom knot"
symbol of wisdom, ingenuity, intelligence and patience

Now that you have been given the prestigious title of the chosen one and you have managed to put together your loved one's healthcare dream team. You may think that you know everything there is to know about your loved one but you might be surprised by what you don't know.

When I first told my friends I was writing this book, I thought it would be a great opportunity to test out my theory about how much they didn't know about the loved ones closest to them. I even quizzed my brother, who had been married to his late wife for 10 years at the time. I found out that my brother had no idea whether or not his wife had any allergies! A friend of mine didn't know his mother's blood type. Yet another friend knew his closest cousin was allergic to an antibiotic but wasn't sure which one. This is vital information to have when you're a caregiver.

Below is a list of the top ten things that you need to know about the person that you are caring for and why it is important know. You must either commit it to memory, or put it in a location where you can quickly and easily access it:

1) Primary Care Physician (PCP) Information

It is essential as a caregiver to be as involved as possible with your loved one's care. One of the best ways to do this is to go with your loved one to their doctor visits--not just the ones when there is a major problem, but some of the routine ones as well. This is especially true if your loved one had a PCP prior to the diagnosis. You will need to make sure that the PCP gets to know you and sees that you are going to be more involved with their patient.

Remember, the information that you will hear at your loved one's doctor visit is confidential. This is why it's very important for you to have two very important documents with you when you go to their doctor's appointment - a signed copy of a healthcare power of attorney and an advance directive. You also need to be listed at each doctor's office as the person who has permission to access any of your loved one's medical records and/or information pertaining to their health. Some doctor's offices require that you use their forms, so call ahead of time and ask which forms they need. Trust me when I tell you that no doctor's office is going to accept your word alone that you are authorized to see your loved one's medical information. Even if it's your very own parent! The HIPAA rule is rock solid.

HIPAA stands for Health Insurance Portability and Accountability Act. It was created in 1996 to protect the privacy of a person's medical records and any other personal health related information. You know when your doctor's office asks you if there is a number they can reach you and then they ask, "Is it okay if I leave a message at this number?" Well, that's HIPAA at its best. In my caregiving journey, I had a love/hate relationship with HIPAA. I was always trying to get information on my mother's health status, and each time I was questioned. A signed medical power of attorney and other documentation helped with my frustration.

Once you have introduced yourself to the PCP and have all the right documentation, make sure that they have all your contact information. Get theirs as well. You need the physician's name and phone number of course, but also their fax number, office hours, and other details that can help with planning and sending documents. It will also help to keep a log of the dates of each doctor visit. A great way to keep track of this information is to check and see if the doctor's office uses an online portal. Through healthcare portals, you can always stay on top of the last time they had a check-up, what the last test results were or even what medication was provided.

2) Allergic Reactions to Medication

As you care for your loved one, you'll continually answer a number of standard questions. One of those questions is, "Are they allergic to any medications?" You must be prepared to answer this question because it will directly affect the medical treatment your loved one receives. Reactions to medications can range from annoying side effects like weight gain to life-threatening effects like suicidal thoughts. So ask your loved one for a complete list of drug reactions and provide this history with their PCP.

Make sure that when discussing these reactions, you get details of exactly what happens to them when they take a medication they are allergic to. Ask them to be as descriptive as possible. For example, if they say the medication makes them itch, ask them if the itching is in one area or if it is all over. Does itching happen quickly or gradually get worse? Make sure you tell the doctor of any reaction to any medications that you know of. Details matter!

3) Medication List

No one expects you to memorize every single medication that your loved one takes; however, it is important to make sure that you maintain a current and active list of any and all medications they are taking at your disposal. This list can be stored electronically or on paper, whichever makes the most sense to you. Should you choose to have an electronic list, there are websites like CVS.com that save an electronic history of current and previous medications your loved one may be taking. You will have to go online and set up an account, but this is a great resource to have because all the information is saved in the system. Again, many doctor's offices have online portals which contain the names and doses of prescribed medication as well. If you prefer to have a medication list on paper, make sure that you not only keep the list somewhere where you can find it, but also keep an additional copy in another location should you lose the original paper. I used to keep an electronic copy and a hardcopy in a binder with all my mother's other medical information. Remember the old school Trapper Keeper from the 80s? That was my smartphone back in the day.

Doctors will need the names of your loved ones the medications and their treatment plans because giving doctors as much information as possible will help them with accurate care of your loved one. I suggest providing the doctor with the name of the medication, the dosage of the medication, the date it was prescribed, and the doctor who prescribed it. It may seem like overkill, but the objective here is to make sure that the doctors caring for your loved one have all the information they need to provide appropriate care.

4) Social Security Number

Identity theft is a real! People don't just steal identities to go shopping and travel. With the cost of healthcare skyrocketing, identity thieves have become creative in stealing identities to order medications as well. Years ago you could just tell the doctor's office that you were the spouse, child, or sibling of their patient and they would take you at your word. Now, with the HIPAA law and fear of identity theft, caregivers can struggle to get and give information from healthcare providers. Everyone hopefully learns early in their lives that under no circumstances should they just haphazardly give out their social security number or any other information that can be used to exploit someone identity. Caregivers, however, need their loved one's social security number.

As a safety precaution, I suggest not keeping their social security card on you. Make it your mission to memorize your loved one's social security number as you do your own.

5) Blood Type

Knowing your loved one's blood type can save their life. Let's suppose your loved one needs a blood transfusion during a medical emergency. Knowing your loved one's blood type and providing this information to the physicians will avoid any unnecessary complications. This becomes even more important if your loved one has a rare blood type like B- or even AB- which is the rarest type. Believe it or not, complications due to blood rejection can be the difference between life and death.

Since blood type information is not anything that someone can steal and use wrongfully, feel free to put this information in your computer or smartphone as well.

6) Location of Important Documents

My ex-boyfriend's mother used to always tell me, "If something happens to me, you can find my life insurance in the vase on my dresser, my birth certificate under the picture of my parents, and my bank information in my top dresser drawer on the left side." As funny as I always thought it was that she hid paperwork around the house, it felt great that she was comfortable enough to share that information with me. Because the reality is, no one is thinking straight when the person they care about is rushed to the hospital.

We will go into detail on all the important documents you will need to have in later chapters but for right now, it is important for you to understand those documents must be together and someplace safe. I used to keep my mother's important documents in a fire-proof, locked box in my apartment. When she lived in a nursing facility, I made sure that the management office had copies of everything that was in my safety deposit box because paperwork has a tendency to get misplaced. You don't want to take your chances with these important documents being damaged, stolen or destroyed.

7) Family Health History

You all know the drill. When you first go to a doctor's office, they give you a stack of paperwork to fill out and without fail there is a section on the form asking about your health history and the health history of specific family members. This is not a time to draw a blank, my fellow caregiver! It is not enough to only know about the health issues of your loved one's parents. Some forms will ask about their grandparents, siblings, even aunts and uncles, so do your homework!

You may not think it is important to know that your grandfather had hypertension and that your grandmother had diabetes, but it is. Family history is a great way for physicians to help in the treatment of patients. Especially when there is a genetic issue involved. It helps give the doctor a clearer roadmap to effective treatment to your loved one.

Back in 2000, I had been working on my family genealogy for about two years and found out some very interesting information about my father's mother – my paternal grandmother. When I reviewed her death certificate, I discovered that she had actually died from "complications due to diabetes." My paternal grandmother never took any medication for diabetes. She never complained about her blood sugar being low or having any of the common symptoms of a diabetic, so none of us had any idea she was diabetic.

Fast forward to three years later, my 7-year-old nephew was losing weight FAST. He had very little appetite and felt thirsty all the time. My brother and his wife first chalked it up to my nephew being nervous about having moved to a new city and starting at a new school. Two days later, my nephew was rushed to the emergency room at a nearby hospital. We found out that he was suffering from diabetic ketoacidosis, and we had gotten him to the hospital just in time. My brother and his wife were shocked and amazed that their son was diagnosed with Type 1 diabetes. To me, it was no surprise because I had just found out both my grandmothers had it. I knew it was bound to show up somewhere in a future generation.

8) Emergency Contacts

As much as you would like to think that you can handle it all in an emergency, you need help. You deserve help. The best caregivers are the ones that know and accept they can't do everything by themselves. You must know exactly who can and will help, and who will just make things more difficult. Talk openly to your loved one about whom they would like to have as their emergency contacts and why. If your family is anything like mine, you will have some people that do nothing but add drama to any situation. If this is the case, keep those family members off your emergency contact list!

Try to make sure your list of emergency contacts is full of both responsible and reliable people. Remember, there is no limit to the number of people that you can have on your list but too many people on the list may make things more complicated. Each person on the emergency contact list should have a copy of the list and they should all be relatively familiar with each other just in case. Remember, these people are a part of your loved one's dream team so you want them to be able to work together effectively in case of a medical emergency.

9) Health Insurance Information

Do you know whether your loved one has an HMO or PPO, Medicaid or Medicare? Are they paying for their health insurance out of pocket, or are they covered by their employer's health insurance? Things like this are important to know. Especially if your loved one is in a position where they cannot answer these questions themselves.

Knowing and understanding the twists and turns of the health insurance industry can be a daunting task even for the most knowledgeable. It will take a bit of research on your part and can be very time consuming. It is important to know that health insurance is divided into a variety of components. It may or may not include dental and vision. If you are able to find a good plan, speak to a social worker or call the plan directly to get assistance in maneuvering through the maze we call health insurance.

Primary caregivers should request an extra insurance card to keep with them at all times. Some health insurance companies will ask for written proof that you are the primary caregiver. After you provide them with this information, they will send you the same health insurance card that your loved one has. Keep these cards with all your other important medical documents.

10) Spiritual Background

Even the military makes sure that they know the spiritual background of their troops. Just check out a soldier's dog tags! This may not seem like an important thing to know, but in moments of crisis, a religious leader can provide immense spiritual and emotional comfort.

Spiritual support is very important in our community. Our culture has sometimes been known to trust the prayer of a spiritual leader over the medical knowledge of a doctor. This could be due to the historical abuse and experimentation on black and brown bodies. I have an aunt who believes if she just prays about her congestive heart failure, it will be fine. I am not doubting her steadfast faith. But as one of my favorite scripture states, "So also faith alone without works is dead." (James 2:17)

If you have a loved one like my aunt, make sure you respect their spiritual beliefs and background. Your loved one's spiritual well-being is connected to their physical health. Take the time to learn what is important to them spiritually - particularly if their beliefs are foreign to you.

Part

4 LEARN
THE
LANGUAGE

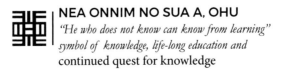

NEA ONNIM NO SUA A, OHU
"He who does not know can know from learning"
symbol of knowledge, life-long education and
continued quest for knowledge

One of the scariest things about becoming a caregiver is the realization of how much you don't know. You have to learn so much so fast. However, you also want to appear knowledgeable, and to inspire confidence in your loved one. I know from several conversations with friends and family that fear of looking stupid can prevent people from asking their doctor questions—or even from seeing the doctor at all. They are worried they will mispronounce medical terms or words and be corrected by a doctor or nurse. I know how my folks are, and I know that Black folks NEVER want to look stupid! This can be particularly true if the health care professional is not a person of color. The truth is if you are a caregiver, not asking questions makes you look stupid! Good care requires you to ask questions. Always ask questions!

With the entertainment industry giving us the ideal doctors like Marcus Welby, MD, Dr. Quinn, and Dr. Huxtable, it is easy to assume that all doctors will explain things to you with ease, humor and charm. That is not always the case, which is why assembling a dream team (as stated in the previous chapter) is so vitality important. It is also important to remember that there are many reasons why people go into the medical profession and helping people is not always the main reason. This means you may run into a healthcare professional in your journey as a caregiver, who doesn't want to answer a ton of your questions, or who seems to rush you out of their office because they have several other patients waiting.

One time I took my mom to the dentist. I pushed my mom, in her wheelchair, to the front desk, so that she could be eye level with the office manager while we checked her in. Both my mother and I greeted the office manage separately with a "Good morning." I told the office manager that we had an appointment and the office manager looked directly at me and casually said, "When's her birthday?" She completely ignored my mother who was sitting right there! My mother immediately straightened herself up in the wheelchair a bit and with a tone I knew so well said, "Her birthday is June 28th!" The office manager rolled her eyes and said, "Thank you, Ms. Jackson."

We've all had these sorts of unpleasant experiences in a doctor's office. As a caregiver, it is your job to ensure that the doctors and other healthcare professionals treat your loved one with dignity and respect. You must also learn the language (medical jargon) of your loved one's specific ailment, and the medical system more generally. Information available on the internet can help you tremendously with this education, of course, but you still have to ask questions when you don't understand something about the information you find. For example, if your loved one goes to the doctor and is told they have a tumor, the doctor will describe the tumor as either malignant or benign. If you don't know the meaning of either of those words, how can you express the severity (or not) of the tumor and what to expect next? Don't guess. Do your research. Ask questions until you fully understand. Your loved one deserves it.

There will always be terms and words and procedures to learn as a caregiver. Sometimes I wish there was a caregiver university where we could all go and just get a degree! But since there is no caregiver universities, you must remember to write down questions before your loved one's doctor's visit, and at the appointment ask a ton of questions. If the doctor says a word or a term that you don't understand, do not be ashamed to ask him/her to repeat the word or spell it so you can look up the meaning later. To this day I still bring my iPad with me to doctor visits and look things up on the Internet. The first time I did that, my doctor was surprised. Now, when I forget my iPad, he writes it down for me to look up later.

In this chapter, I am going to provide you with a very small but important glossary of medical terms, definitions of medical professionals, and medical synonyms/antonyms that will help get you started on your journey of learning the language of caregiving. A special shout out to F.A. Davis for giving me permission to add these terms to my book! Please understand that this glossary is by no means exhaustive. It will, however, get you started. I even put a quick little quiz at the end so you can see how well you catch on.

Caregiver Starter Glossary
SOURCE: Taber's Cyclopedic Medical Dictionary 22nd Edition

advance directive
A written document in the form of a living will or durable power of attorney prepared by a competent person and specifying what, if any, extraordinary procedures, surgeries, medications, or treatments the patient desires in the future if the patient should become incompetent to make such decisions.

anemia
A reduction in the mass of circulating red blood cells. People are considered anemic when their hemoglobin levels are more than two standard deviations below the mean level in their hospital's laboratory.

antibiotic
A natural or synthetic substance that destroys microorganisms or inhibits their growth. Antibiotics are used extensively to treat infectious diseases in plants, animals, and humans.

aspiration
The inhalation of fluid or solid objects into the lower airways or lungs. This may occur in people with impaired gag reflexes or other swallowing disorders and also in neonates with meconium present in the amniotic fluid.

atrophy
To degenerate; lose size, strength, or vitality.

benign
Not recurrent or progressive; nonmalignant.

biopsy
A tissue sample removed from the body for microscopic examination, usually to establish a diagnosis. The tissue can be obtained surgically or by aspiration. The procedure can be guided by computed tomography, ultrasonography, magnetic resonance imaging, or radiography, or it can be performed blind (without imaging).

cancer
Malignant neoplasia marked by the uncontrolled growth of cells, often with invasion of healthy tissues locally or throughout the body.

catheter
A tube passed into the body for evacuating or injecting fluids. It may be made of elastic, elastic web, rubber, glass, metal, or plastic.

chemistry panel
A group of routine laboratory tests that assess commonly measured electrolytes, e.g., the concentrations of sodium or potassium in the blood; kidney function, e.g., BUN or creatinine; glucose; or liver function.

chemotherapy
Drug therapy used to treat infections, cancers, and other diseases and conditions. *Chemotherapeutic agents to treat cancer are toxic or poisons and pose risks to those who handle them, primarily pharmacists and nurses.*

colonoscopy
Visualization of the lower gastrointestinal tract. The procedure usually consists of the insertion of a flexible endoscope through the anus to inspect the entire colon and terminal ileum. The procedure detects polyps in 5 to 10% of screened patients and cancer in about 0.5 to 1.0%. Because these lesions can be removed during the examination, it is a proven, effective means of reducing the risk of death from colorectal cancers.

cyst
A closed sac or pouch with a definite wall, containing fluid, semifluid, or solid material. It is usually an abnormal structure resulting from developmental anomalies, obstruction of ducts, or parasitic infection.

dehydration
The clinical consequences of negative fluid balance, i.e., of fluid intake that fails to match fluid loss.

dementia
A progressive, irreversible decline in mental function.

diabetes mellitus
A chronic metabolic disorder marked by hyperglycemia. DM results either from failure of the A general term for diseases marked by excessive urination and elevated blood sugar, esp. diabetes mellitus (DM).

dialysis
The diffusion of blood across a semipermeable membrane to remove toxic materials and to maintain fluid, electrolyte, and acid-base balance in cases of impaired kidney function or absence of the kidneys.

diarrhea
The passage of fluid or unformed stools.

edema
A local or generalized condition in which body tissues contain an excessive amount of tissue fluid in the interstitial spaces.

emphysema
A chronic obstructive pulmonary disease marked by an abnormal increase in the size of air spaces distal to the terminal bronchiole, with destruction of the alveolar walls. These changes result in a loss of the normal elastic properties of the lungs and difficulty exhaling

air. Alveolar septa are destroyed, and portions of the capillary bed are eliminated. Residual volume increases.An overwhelming sustained feeling of exhaustion and diminished capacity for physical and mental work.

exacerbation
Aggravation of symptoms or increase in the severity of a disease.

fatigue
An overwhelming sustained feeling of exhaustion and diminished capacity for physical and mental work.

hospice
An interdisciplinary program of palliative care and supportive services that addresses the physical, spiritual, social, and economic needs of terminally ill patients and their families.

hyperglycemia
Abnormally high blood sugar levels. Hyperglycemia can cause numerous unwanted effects. It can impair wound healing; decrease the body's ability to fight infections; worsen the neurological deficits found in stroke; increase the risk of death in critically ill patients; and damage the kidneys, peripheral nerves, retinae, blood vessels, and heart.

hypertension
In adults, a condition in which the blood pressure (BP) is higher than 140 mm Hg systolic or 90 mm Hg diastolic on three separate readings recorded several weeks apart.

hyperthyroidism
A disease caused by excessive levels of thyroid hormone in the body.

hypoglycemia
An abnormally low level of glucose in the blood, often associated

with neurological side effects and arousal of the sympathetic nervous system. Medication-induced hypoglycemia is a common occurrence during the treatment of diabetes mellitus.

hypothyroidism
The clinical consequences of inadequate levels of thyroid hormone in the body. Chronic or acute thyroid deficiency causes diminished basal metabolism, intolerance of cold temperatures, fatigue, mental apathy, physical sluggishness, constipation, muscle aches, dry skin and hair, and coarsening of features.

infarction
Death of tissue from deprivation of its blood supply.

impaction
A condition of being tightly wedged into a part, as when the eruption of a tooth is blocked by other teeth or when an organ is overloaded, as the bowels by feces.

incontinence
Loss of self-control, especially of urine, feces, or semen.

infusion
Any liquid substance (other than blood) introduced into the body for therapeutic purposes.

insulin
A hormone secreted by the beta cells of the pancreas. As a drug, insulin is used principally to control diabetes mellitus.

invasive
Pertaining to an incision, penetration, or puncture of the body or one of its parts, e.g., during a procedure.

ketoacidosis

Acidosis due to an excess of ketone bodies. It occurs in individuals who do not produce adequate insulin to sustain normal fat metabolism. Symptoms typically include nausea, vomiting, excessive urination, rapid breathing, and dehydration.

malignant

Growing worse; resisting treatment, said of cancerous growths. Tending or threatening to produce death; harmful.

Methicillin-Resistant Staphylococcus Aureus (MRSA)

MRSA is a common cause of boils (skin abscesses) and an occasional cause of pneumonia. MRSA is resistant to most antibiotics and is usually acquired in hospitals or nursing homes, where it may be spread from patient to patient by contaminated hands, clothing, and equipment.

Multiple Sclerosis (MS)

A chronic disease of the central nervous system (CNS) in which there is destruction of myelin within several regions of the brain and spinal cord at different times. This results in temporary, repetitive, or sustained disruptions in nerve impulse conduction, causing symptoms such as muscular weakness, loss of coordination, numbness, visual disturbances, loss of control of bowel, bladder, and sexual functions.

ombudsman

In medicine, an advocate, esp. for patients or clients of health care institutions. The ombudsman verifies complaints and advocates for their resolution.

paralysis

Loss of purposeful movement, usually as a result of neurological disease (such as strokes, spinal cord injuries, poliomyelitis), drugs, or toxins. Loss of motor function may be complete (paralysis) or partial (paresis), unilateral (hemiplegic) or bilateral (diplegic), confined to the lower extremities (paraplegic) or present in all four extremities (quadriplegic), accompanied by increased muscular tension and hyperactive reflexes (spastic) or by loss of reflexes and tone (flaccid).

pressure ulcer
Damage to the skin or underlying structures from compression of tissue and inadequate perfusion.

reflux
A return or backward flow.

remission
The period during which symptoms abate.

respiration
The act of breathing (inhaling and exhaling) during which the lungs are provided with air through inhaling and the carbon dioxide is removed through exhaling. Normal respiratory exchange of oxygen and carbon dioxide in the lungs is impossible unless the pulmonary tissue is adequately perfused with blood.

shunt
An anomalous passage or one artificially constructed to divert flow from one main route to another.

stroke
A sudden loss of neurological function, caused by vascular injury (loss of blood flow) to an area of the brain.

tremor
An involuntary movement of a part or parts of the body resulting from alternate contractions of opposing muscles.

tumor
An abnormal mass. Growth or proliferation that is independent of

neighboring tissues is a hallmark of all tumors, benign and malignant.

urinalysis
Analysis of the urine.

vertigo
The sensation of moving around in space (subjective vertigo) or of having objects move about the person (objective vertigo). Vertigo is sometimes inaccurately used as a synonym for dizziness, lightheadedness, or giddiness. It may be caused by a variety of entities, including middle ear disease; toxic conditions such as those caused by salicylates, alcohol, or streptomycin; sunstroke; postural hypotension; or toxemia due to food poisoning or infectious diseases.

That's Short for What?

So now you've taken a look at some of the medical terms you might hear while attending a doctor visit with your loved one. Have you heard some of these words used before? Have you been using any terms incorrectly? It is my hope that while using this guide, you will become familiar with most (if not all!) of these terms and start to build upon your understanding of medical terminology. If you do, before you know it, conversations with medical professionals will be a little less intimidating and a lot more informative.

Let's look at something else that tends to make new caregivers nervous. Acronyms. Even after having been a caregiver for over 20 years, there are still times where I come across one of these acronyms and I am like, "Come on! Who could possibly know that?" It is okay if you don't know every acronym you see. But these terms aren't going away, so let's get you started on learning some commons ones.

The acronyms below are often used in the language of medical treatment, insurance, and refer to physician/nurse titles. Feel free to add your own in the back of this guide in the notes section.

Common Acronyms

SOURCE: Taber's Cyclopedic Medical Dictionary 22nd Edition

PPO Preferred Provider Organization
HMO Health Maintenance Organization
EOB Explanation of Benefits
MD Doctor of Medicine
DO Doctor of Osteopathic Medicine
RN Registered Nurse
LPN Licensed Practical Nurse
LVN Licensed Vocational Nurse
PA Physician's Assistant
NP Nurse Practitioner
LSW Licensed Social Worker
CNA Certified Nurses Assistant
HHA Home Health Aide
PCP Primary Care Physician
DME Durable Medical Equipment
SSI Supplemental Security Income
SSDI Social Security Disability Insurance
SSN Social Security Number
OOP Out-of-Pocket
HIPPA Health Insurance Portability and Accountability Act of 1996
ER Emergency Room
EMS Emergency Medical Services
PT Physical Therapy
OT Occupational Therapy
RX Prescription Drug
DNR Do Not Resuscitate

This Stuff Again?

If you thought you were done with learning prefixes and suffixes like you did in elementary school, you thought wrong! They are back to help you break down some of the diagnoses, prognoses and treatments that your loved one's physician may tell you about. Long medical names and terms may look impossible to understand (let alone say), but not if you break them down in little pieces. You don't need a college or medical degree to understand them. You just need patience and energy to look them up.

Consider how the word otorhinolaryngology breaks down into parts that can tell you all you need to know about the word:

otos, "ear", rhis, "nose", larynx, "larynx" and logia, "study"

So that means it is the study of the ear, nose and throat. Impressive, right? Let's look at some more prefixes and suffixes that will expand your medical vocabulary.

Medical Prefixes to Know

PREFIX	MEANING	PREFIX	MEANING
Endo-	inside	Intra-	within
Inter-	between	Peri-	around
Pneum-	lung	Cardi-	heart
Stomat-	mouth	Gastro-	stomach
Renal-	kidneys	Phleb-	veins
Hem-/Hemat-	blood	Neuron-	nerves
Angio-	vessels	Arthro-	joints

SOURCE: Taber's Cyclopedic Medical Dictionary 22nd Edition

Medical Suffixes to Know

SUFFIX	MEANING	SUFFIX	MEANING
-osis	process, condition, state	-pathy	disease
-logy	study of	-lepsy	seizure
-itis	inflammation	-ism	condition, disease
-ectomy	the surgical removal of something	-algia	pain
-gram/graph	record of picture	-trophy	nourishment, development

SOURCE: Taber's Cyclopedic Medical Dictionary 22nd Edition

Test Yourself

Neuralgia means : _____

Cardiology means : _____

Gastritis means : _____

Part

5

A DIFFERENT KIND OF "TREATMENT"

HWE MU DUA
"measuring stick"
symbol of examination and quality control

Even on my most politically correct days, writing about healthcare disparities is difficult. This is not fake news, nor is it me—or any other Black person for that matter--being overly sensitive. There are still scenarios in which a patient of color will be treated differently by a healthcare professional whose unconscious bias dictates care. Unfortunately, you as a caregiver of color need to be aware of this and pay close attention to the quality of care that your loved one is receiving. Not just because of what they may have or what kind of health insurance they have, but also because of who they are.

The medical profession historically has not always been kind or fair to people of color. Are you ready for a history lesson?

HeLA Cells (1951) *(Sloot, 2010)* – Henrietta Lacks was a poor Black tobacco farmer whose cells were taken from her without her knowledge. Yet these cells have contributed greatly to medical knowledge about vaccines, genes, and much more. Henrietta was never compensated for those valuable cells.

Tuskegee Experiment (1932-1972) *(Centers for Disease Control and Prevention, 2015)* – The Public Health service and The Tuskegee Institute embarked on a study of the "natural" history of syphilis by following 600 Black men. Of these 600 Black men, 399 of them were infected with syphilis and were told that they were being treated for "bad blood." They never consented to the treatment but were persuaded to participate with the promise of free exams, food, and burial insurance. But they didn't get treatment. They were allowed to suffer and die from a treatable disease.

I do not want you to be paranoid about the medical profession, but I do want you to understand why, if you are caring for an older African American relative, they might be a bit apprehensive to volunteer for medical trials, not want to take certain medications, or even want a second opinion. This history of the medical exploitation of African Americans and the current healthcare disparities based on class and race, combined with our tendency to put everything (and everyone!)

before our health, is a recipe for disaster.

When I read of these medical atrocities of the past, it makes me angry! Not just because people died or that they suffered in their lives, but because there are specific patterns in these situations. In many of these cases, the Black people were at the mercy of the physicians involved. Black people were vulnerable financially. They needed money to eat, pay bills and care for their families. They were also vulnerable academically. They were not aware of what to ask or what was allowed by doctors. Our trust of doctors when in these positions has proven to be lethal to our health. Unfortunately, knowledge of how we as a people have been taken advantage of has moved us from one extreme to another and now, we are practically killing ourselves because of our lack of trust of physicians (Roberts Kennedy, PhD, APRN, BC, Clomus Mathis, PhD, & Woods, MSN, 2007).

Your probably sitting thinking, "It's not our fault that we don't trust doctors. Look at what they have done to us!" Okay, I will agree with you that some of the stuff done to us as a people has been unethical, painful and outright evil but, we need to take seriously the quote by a man named George Santayana who said, "Those who do not learn history are doomed to repeat it." We cannot sit and not go to the doctor because "they don't give us good care". We have to understand as much as we can about the health profession, ask questions about what we don't understand and take better care of ourselves.

The following chart from the Center for Disease Control (CDC) shows us just how scary the differences are compared to our White and Non-White counterparts. We have heard how we are at higher risk for things like Diabetes but this chart is very helpful is showing just how much.

Even on my most politically correct days, writing about healthcare disparities is difficult.

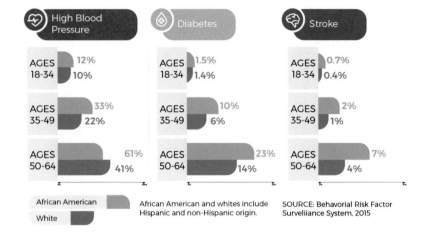

High Blood Pressure		Diabetes		Stroke	
AGES 18-34	12% / 10%	AGES 18-34	1.5% / 1.4%	AGES 18-34	0.7% / 0.4%
AGES 35-49	33% / 22%	AGES 35-49	10% / 6%	AGES 35-49	2% / 1%
AGES 50-64	61% / 41%	AGES 50-64	23% / 14%	AGES 50-64	7% / 4%

African American / White

African American and whites include Hispanic and non-Hispanic origin.

SOURCE: Behavorial Risk Factor Surveliiance System, 2015

Very interesting when you look at it this way, huh? These are just a few health issues that we as Black people suffer from the most. I bet you know of at least 4 or 5 people in your immediate families that have had at least one of these health issues in their lives. The scary part is that these illnesses are bad on their own but if they go untreated…well, it's not good.

As caregivers, we are not just people who take care of someone we love. We are advocates for positive change in healthcare, enforcers of fair healthcare legislation, and mediators between our loved ones and the healthcare professionals that provide medical advice and treatment. Yes, we are all that!

We must remember, however, that in order for us to be effective, we have to continue to be in a constant state of learning and be hyper-aware of the healthcare disparities that exist. I will give you a personal example. I was very young when my mother was diagnosed with Multiple Sclerosis and at the time, there was information around for people with MS but not a lot of it about the Black experience. Yes, there is a "Black experience" of MS. I would look for information on how MS would affect my mother in the years to come and as time would go by, I found what she was experiencing was slightly different than what I had being reading about. I would run into people who had MS and they didn't move like my mom or be in the hospital like my mom. Years later, I would find out that even though MS was largely associated with people of European descent, studies show that MS is especially active in African Americans. African Americans with MS are (National Multiple Sclerosis Society, 2018):

• more likely to experience more relapses[1]
• more likely to experience greater disability
• have a greater risk of progressing to require ambulatory assistance earlier
• more likely to develop involvement of the optic nerves and spinal cord (optic-spinal MS) and inflammation of the spinal cord (transverse myelitis).

So, you see, illnesses and their symptoms can be different for us. Now, I would be naïve if I told you that doctors treat all their patients the same. I would also be naïve if I told you that throughout your job as caregiver, you will not run into people who will make your job difficult simply because you are a person of color. As a society, we have a long way to go when it comes to treating each other fairly so do not assume that this is not also the case in reference to health care.

What am I saying? Be aware. Educate yourself. Know your rights. And finally, when you do learn something that is helpful, share it! Your fellow caregivers could always use information you may have acquired. It can help for other caregivers to know if there is a doctor you have interacted with that is sensitive to cultural differences. Social media and websites such as www.ratemds.com can help you to share the good, the bad and the ugly of healthcare professionals as well as

1. An exacerbation of MS (also known as a relapse, attack or flare-up) causes new symptoms or the worsening of old symptoms. It can be very mild, or severe enough to interfere with a person's ability to function at home and at work. No two exacerbations are alike, and symptoms vary from person to person and from one exacerbation to another.

their office managers and facilities.

Listen to me and listen to me good, my caregiver friend. You and your loved one deserve good treatment whether or not you make six figures or if you are on public assistance. You don't need a lot of degrees to learn how to take care of your loved one. You just have to have a desire to do the best you can and to be willing to ask questions. Do not be intimidated by the degrees on the doctor's wall. Do not be intimidated by the medical terms that you will hear flow out of the healthcare professional's mouths. Remember to breathe, write everything down, look for the healthcare professionals that have your best interest at heart (no matter what you look like!) and remember – you deserve good care.

Part 6
ORGANIZE YOUR LIFE

DAME-DAME
"name of a board game"
symbol of intelligence and ingenuity

My friends and relatives constantly complain about their disorganization. I shake my head at the friend who can never seem to get to events on time, my aunt who thinks the best place to keep her birth certificate is in her hat box, and even my very own brother who, all of his life, spent his time trying to convince my mother and I that his room, backpack, and his car were in some sort of "organized chaos".

We learn to be organized as children so that we can be responsible. We learn to be organized as caregivers so that we can improve our loved one's quality of life. Organization can be life-saving. When I was a teenager, I used to carry around a Palm Pilot that contained all of the information I needed about my mother (all the things we spoke about in Chapter 3 of this guide). One day, she was rushed to the hospital because of a terrible fever. They found out that she had some sort of infection and needed antibiotics right away. Luckily, I had my Palm Pilot on me and not only a list of all her medications, who prescribed them, how many milligrams of each medicine she took and what each medicine was for, I also had what medications she was allergic to. Thank goodness because they were about to give my mother Cipro, and she was terribly allergic to it!

No matter what degree of caregiving you have to do, there will always be a need for some sort of organization.

So let's talk about how to get you organized. Are you as organized as you would like to be? Are you as organized as you need to be? Here's a good way to tell. If someone had to step into your role as caregiver right now, let's say you were going on a vacation or something, would they be able to function as well as you, or would they have to call you every five minutes for help? Everybody isn't naturally organized and may have to learn ways to improve.

Even though I was organized most my life, becoming a caregiver showed me a whole new side of being organized. Not only did I have to organize, but I also had to be creative with it. In Chapter 2, I taught you about the top ten things you need to know about the loved one you are caring for. Here, I am going to build upon that information and teach you what I know about organization and how being organized helped me keep things together when things were getting kind of hectic. Tweak things as necessary. Think outside of the box to devise a solution that alleviates some of the pressures of caregiving.

The Getaway Bag

Going to the hospital may be inevitable. As we all know, hospitals are absolutely no fun at all. Between the stresses of supporting your loved one emotionally and getting coordinated with doctors and nurses about your loved one's care, it's easy to feel overwhelmed.

Being as organized as you can be can take away a bit of this stress. Enter the "getaway bag." This item is the indirect brainchild of my mother, who was extremely modest and complained constantly about hospital socks that always fall off, the "little teeny comb that can't do anything to a person's head", and the hospital gown that "doesn't cover a thing." As the hospital stays became more and more frequent, so did the request for more personal items to make the hospital stay as comfortable as possible.

The concept of the getaway bag is simple. Get a bag that you won't miss. I gave my mom an old gym bag of mine since it was easy to connect to the back of her wheelchair. In this bag you put any items that your loved one would need to make their not-so-great-stay at the hospital better. For example, my mother was obsessed with not looking bad in the hospital. She would say, "I can feel bad, but I don't have to LOOK bad!" So, in her getaway bag we had a few rollers, hair gel, a scarf, headband, rubber bands, comb, and brush. I also included things like Noxema for her face so when she got washed in the morning she could have almost the same experience as she would have at home. This seems like a little thing to you but to have a bit of consistency in your loved one's life preserves their dignity and their sense of control.

There is no limit to the things you put in your bag. As I stated earlier, the whole concept of the getaway bag came from my mother's modesty. She hated being exposed in any fashion so, I made sure that there was always one of her favorite nightgowns in the bag as well. I am sure hospital employees will frown upon me telling you to pack a gown or pajamas since their exposing gowns make it easier for them to work with IVs and examine certain areas of the body, but believe me when I tell you, a happy patient is a healthy patient. If wearing a favorite pajama top will help with the healing process, then do what you can to make that happen. Make sure you talk with the nurses on staff about why you'd like to have your loved one in their own pajamas or nightgown. Remember that your loved one is entitled to wear their own clothes, to groom themselves as they please, and to do what works for them. Being hospitalized does not take away your loved one's right to their own body.

There are so many other items you could pack in your getaway bag, but it is up to you to determine what to pack. A few suggested items are;

- One complete outfit
- Socks
- Hair products/accessories
- Toothbrush
- Book/Magazine

After your bag is packed with all the "homey" things that your loved one would want or need, put it somewhere accessible. The idea is to have it available when the time comes for your loved one to be admitted to the hospital. In my mother's case, she liked the idea that she was in control of the getaway bag, so the bag stayed at her house. She would tell the home health aide or the ambulance people, "Please grab my hospital bag." It preserved her sense of control, and her dignity.

Labels and Lists for Rehabilitation or Nursing Facility Stays

If for some reason your loved one lives in a nursing facility or has to stay in a nursing facility for an extended amount of time, you will really need to be on top of your game. Nursing facilities have to care for a large number of residents, which means managing the property of these residents as well. There is no way the staffers will always be able to differentiate your loved one's items from another's. So it is up to you to make sure that your loved one's items and clothing don't end up in someone else's room. Look at it this way, anything without your loved one's name on it is fair game to any other resident (or staffer) in a nursing facility. I learned this the hard way once when I noticed that one of the residents in the facility my mom was staying in had on her blouse. I knew it was my mom's because I had just bought it for her, but because my mom's name wasn't in the collar, there was nothing I could do. Needless to say, I was furious I couldn't get the blouse back, but I never had the problem again!

I would suggest putting labels or name tags on everything your loved one owns. From socks to their toothbrush to their shoes. Seriously. There is one particular website I used to go to for ordering labels for all my mother's items – www.LabelYourStuff.com has a great array of labels for not just clothing but for waterproof items, bags, shoes, etc. They even offer gift certificates if you know of someone who could use labels.

Your organizational skills should not stop there. Since your loved one will be interacting with a variety of people in their nursing facility, rehabilitation center, or even in the hospital, it is important that you know each of the people who will be in charge of every aspect of your loved one's care —from the person who is in charge of the entire facility to the person who is preparing the meals. You may not need to contact these people on a daily basis, but having at least their name is good information on hand just in case. Again, I used to keep all this information on my Palm Pilot, but if you prefer to write it down instead, get a special notebook (or use the back of this guide) for just this type of information and carry it with you at all times.

A Document Secret Hiding Place

It is funny because when I was younger, I can clearly remember my grandmother having a "secret stash" of important documents. I wasn't really supposed to know where it was, but I just happened to be in the right place at the right time, and I overheard my grandmother talking about them to one of her daughters. Years later, I heard my ex-boyfriend's mother, who was in her late 60's at the time, explain in detail where she had "hidden" her important papers in case of an emergency. As caregivers, we need to take a lesson from our older folks. Keeping your important documentation in a safe, hidden place is a very good idea. Now of course, we no longer have to hide documents under the mattress, in a vase, or as my aunt used to do, in the hat box. We can get safe deposit boxes or even a locked box in the garage. The organized caregiver always keeps all the important medical and personal documents of their loved one in one place and keeps copies with them just in case.

I had a fire-retardant, locked box in my apartment, in which I kept my mother's birth certificate, Social Security card, copies of her Power of Attorney and Living Will, and any forms that had to do with her nursing facility and medical records. I was the only person who had the key to this locked box, because the contents were so important. However, if anything happened to me, I had a copy of that key in my bank safe deposit box so that someone I trusted could get to it if necessary.

The Magic Medicine List

You already know that you need to keep a running list of all the medications that your loved one takes, but I want to suggest that you go a little further than just having a generic list. The list of medications should provide both the generic and name brand name of the medication, the doctor who prescribed it, what your loved one is taking the medicine for, how often the medicine is taken, and the dosage and timing of the drug. You should also note your next appointment with the prescribing physician.

Another very important part of this list should be the names of the medications that your loved one is allergic to. I would even suggest that you note what sort of symptoms your loved one had when they found out they were allergic (itching, blurry vision, hallucinations). My suggestion to you would be for you to keep an electronic list of medications.

Emergency Contact Card

For those people who are not necessarily "techy people," I suggest using what I call my emergency contact card. My aunt, who believed in keeping absolutely everything in her purse (and in her Bible for that matter!), was the inspiration for this card. On the front of my mother's emergency contact card was a list of three emergency contacts, including their full name, home phone number, cell phone number, and work number. The people on this card were listed in the order of closest proximity to her home to make sure that the person closest to her was notified of any emergencies first. It just doesn't make sense to call someone who is the furthest away in an emergency situation.

On the back of the emergency contact card was my mother's diagnosis of Multiple Sclerosis, the contact information for her primary doctor, and the contact information for her neurologist.

There was also a list of what she was allergic to. You might think that all of this information won't fit on a small card but I was able to fit it all on a card the size of a credit card.

It helps to have this card laminated and in a small size so that your loved one can keep it conveniently in his or her wallet. Before making the emergency contact card, go to the people you are thinking of adding as emergency contacts and ask them if it is alright to have

EMERGENCY CONTACT CARD FOR:

NAME:

CONTACT 1:

CONTACT 2:

CONTACT 3:

EMERGENCY CONTACT CARD FOR:
NAME:

DISABILITY/
AILMENT:

ALLERGIES:

DR.'S NAME:

DR.'S PHONE:

them as an emergency contact. Once you have received permission from your emergency contacts, be sure that they all know each other. You want to make sure that the lines of communication are open with everyone so that there are no surprises when an emergency may happen. Let them know that you appreciate them agreeing to help you with the care of your loved one. Maybe even send them a thank you card or note every once in a while. After all, they are now a part of your loved one's dream team.

The Just-in-Case Files

I am pretty proud to say that I had the most extensive "just-in-case" files anyone has ever seen. This file (or files depending on how much information you need to retain) will contain all the paperwork you need to keep you, as a caregiver, organized. My files contained folders for things like the name of the local supermarkets that had delivery services and grocery list of items that my mom liked. There was also a folder of all my mother's clothing sizes, just in case someone wanted to help me with shopping for clothes for her. Another folder was for all the pharmacies that my mother and I used and which ones carried what durable medical products she needed. I even had a folder that contained a list of some of my mother's favorite television shows that she would like to listen to just in case she had a new home health aide.

This just-in-case file was a great help to me if I ever had to leave for weekend trips or work trips. It put me at ease because I knew that everything to care for my mother was in these files. Believe it or not, these files would also put at ease anyone who would be checking in on my mom when I was out of town because they had everything at their disposal to aid my mom with anything she needed. These files, for them, took the fear out of the unknown.

If you are caring for more than one person, consider color coding things to make it easier to find information in your files for each specific person. And as always, make sure you keep this information someplace in your home or apartment where it will be safe. It would be terrible to have all this information organized and ready for whenever you need it and then find out that a child ripped it up or worse, the dog ate it!

Some of you are probably reading this and thinking to yourself, "Oh my goodness! I have never been that organized in my life!" It's okay. Remember that breathing exercise I told you about in chapter one? You might want to take a second to do that now.

The good news is that you can absolutely learn to be organized and believe it or not, you will get better and better at it over time. You might make a few mistakes at first though so don't be so hard on yourself. One time when I thought I had it all together, I went to the doctor with my mom and completely forgot to bring her medicine list. I felt like a fish out of water and like an idiot because I had spent so much time working on it. Another time when my mom was in the hospital, I couldn't remember the name of the place where we ordered her medical supplies. It happens, believe me, to the best of us. Like I said, you are not going to be perfect and no one expects you to be. Just know that you need to be flexible and to make sure when you do make a mistake or forget something that you should notate it and come up with ways that will make it easier to not to make that same mistake again.

Part

7 EMOTIONAL ROLLER-COASTER

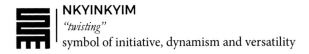

NKYINKYIM
"twisting"
symbol of initiative, dynamism and versatility

One of the first emotions I remember having as a young caregiver was my sense of helplessness. I remember one day, my mother was trying to get out of the bath tub and when she realized that she was too weak from the hot water to dry herself off and get out of the tub, she called me in to help her. At first for me it seemed a simple task since, in my mind, I was only there to be her support. She had always been able to balance herself on the side of the tub, dry herself off, transfer to the toilet and then transfer herself to the wheelchair. Simple to me it seemed. But this time was different. I could tell by the way she called me.

When I came into the bathroom to begrudgingly help her, I sort of just gave her my arm thinking I only needed to help a little. When she began to place all her weight on me, I was surprised but felt I could handle it. But the more weight she put on me, the more we slipped. I felt her weight. I felt her frustration. I began to get frustrated myself as we both continued to slip back into the bath tub. I remember thinking "Oh God. I have to do this but I can't. I can't do this on my own." It was like trying to fight the sea with a sailboat. At that particular moment, my brother must have heard us struggling and he asked if we were ok. I disappointingly said we needed help and he came in to give us both a hand. Of course, my mother being a modest woman, especially in front of her son, covered herself up with a towel. "Don't get shy now!" he said as he made us both laugh. Something both my mother and I needed at that time. Together, we got my mom out of the tub and comfortably in her room and into her warm pajamas.

This tumbling, helpless feeling is a lot like the emotional rollercoaster of caregiving. When I remember the bathtub story, it reminds me of the type of helplessness that we caregivers feel and it almost makes us angry because we feel that we should be able to do a task that seems easy but we can't. As Black people we sometimes have a tendency to feel that if we try something and we can't do it, we are failures. I know in that moment I was thinking, "Come on Ky'a get it together!

You have helped her out of the tub before, what is wrong with you!?" What I didn't consider until years later was the helplessness my mother was feeling. As a strong black woman, my mother's pride was probably bruised because she had to ask for help in the first place. And then, on top of that, she then had to feel embarrassed because her son had to help as well. It was hard for me to think of how she was feeling at that time but I saw it later and I am hoping that my example will help you not to make the same mistake I did.

As a caregiver, you will experience a rollercoaster of emotions no matter how good you get at doing the job. Some days, you will feel like you can't go on. Some days you will feel like you are all alone in this fight to care for your loved one. At the same time, there will be days where you look at your loved one and are simply happy they are still here with you. Happy that you can hold them and love them another day. There may even be some days where you are so organized and so on top of your game that you might be proud of the caregiver you have become.

There a ton of highs and lows with this job called caregiving. One day you could be on top of the world because perhaps your loved one isn't in as much pain or because they were having a good day personally and the next day, it could just be bad for both of you and everything could be going wrong. You can go from feeling tired, to feeling happy, to feeling sad all within the same week. Well hell, in some cases in the same day! As I look back at my caregiving experience, I remember the emotion I felt most was anger. I managed to figure out ways to get through the other emotions I felt during my early caregiving years. If I was sad, I would listen to music. If I was stressed, my organizational skills helped me to figure out how to feel less stressed but the anger, I just never could get control of that. I was angry at the fact that I had to watch my mother, a woman I considered to be the strongest woman in the world, struggle. I was angry that Multiple Sclerosis wasn't curable. I was angry that I had to do most of the caregiving by myself. That there wasn't another adult who could help me understand how to navigate my caregiver journey. Angry that I felt so alone.

I want to tell you something that I wish someone had told me when I started my caregiving journey. Whatever you are feeling, it's ok. Whether it be anger, sadness, frustration, exhaustion. It's okay to feel all of those things but it is not okay to get stuck in those feelings and certainly not okay to take those feelings out on your loved one. When I was a first-time caregiver, I didn't know that it was okay to feel these emotions and as a way to "handle" them, I would simply keep them inside. Not smart at all! The emotions just began to swell and then the more I suppressed them, the more my body would react physically. It is because of my suppressing these emotions that at the tender age of fifteen I had three ulcers. Then as the years went on, the ulcers went away and the emotional stress manifested itself as migraine headaches. Emotional stress and holding in your feelings can be the body's worst nightmare. That is why it is important as a caregiver to do things to manage your emotional load (Weinstein, 2018). It took me several years to understand this and to learn ways to release my emotions. I want to share with you a few things that you can do if you begin to feel emotionally stressed.

Talk About It

Now I know as Black folks, it is hard for us to open up to other people. Particularly when we tend to be so private about the things that show us as vulnerable. But being prideful about your vulnerability and holding everything in is one of those things that could create emotional, spiritual, and physical damage. Listen friend, you have got to make sure that you have at least one or two people to confide in when things are getting tough. Whether it be your best friend, your therapist, or your pastor. I will be honest with you, sometimes finding a confidant is tough. Particularly if you want a confidant that will not share what you are going through with other people. We as Black people tend to want our private information to stay private and often times, sharing our private fears and emotions turn out to be disastrous if we share them with the wrong person. This sort thing happened to me once and I will never forget it. But the solution is not to be distrustful of everyone and continue to hold things in. The solution is to be more careful about who you choose as your confidant. I have found that some of the best confidants are other caregivers. Even though we may not have experienced the exact same things, there are some common things among caregivers that you can share that will help alleviate the isolation and loneliness and, in some cases, the anger. When you get together with other caregivers, it's almost like how it is when divorcees gather to share war stories about their divorces or how men share stories in the barbershop. This camaraderie with other caregivers will take some of the stress off and will allow you, even if only for a little while, to feel a little less alone in your caregiver journey.

Now I know that when I mentioned therapy earlier, some of you reading this made a face and were probably like, "I don't need no therapy! I'm not crazy!" If that thought popped into your mind, I'm gonna need you to stop it! Black people for generations have gone through life toughing it out and not seeking psychological help because of this antiquated way of thinking. Going to therapy and talking out your problems, concerns, and issues does not mean you are crazy. It does not mean you can't handle things. It does not mean weakness. It simply means that you want to become more self-aware and acquire tools that will help you get to the source of what concerns, motivates and inspires you. Nowhere in that statement do you hear "crazy" so, stop it! Therapy can be healing and cathartic, and even though it may not be for everyone, therapy is truly a good way to talk about the emotions you are feeling as a caregiver so please do not rule it out. If you have the opportunity to go to therapy, by all means, go.

Work Out

It is a known fact that working out helps your body to be physically fit. It also helps your emotional wellbeing. Going to the gym will do wonders for you not only because it gets your adrenaline pumping but it also allows you a change of atmosphere and the opportunity to decompress from the pressures that caregiving can bring. Now before you tell me that you don't really have time to go to the gym, let me give a little more clarity to what I mean when I say work out. It doesn't mean you have to spend a full-on day at the gym. You can take a 10-minute walk outside or do some stretching (or yoga) at home if you can't get to the gym. The idea is to get your heart rate up and pumping. So, if dancing around the house while doing chores is the only way you can get some exercise in your day, then put your headphones on, turn on your favorite music, and do some dance cardio. This way you can get some housework done and take care of yourself at the same time. When I was a caregiver to my mother, she used to have to go to both physical and occupational therapy. As a way to support her as well as get my own time working out, I would coordinate my gym time to when she had to go to physical therapy. This way we both had stories to share after our workouts about how our respective trainers tried to kill us. It made for productive time separately and quality time together. You can figure out a way to take care of yourself. You just need to be very creative.

Eat Right

Since we are now family, I need to continue to be honest with you when I say that I am not the healthiest eater in the world. Don't judge me! Although I have gotten much better at eating a little healthier over the years, when I started out as a caregiver I had no idea that what I was eating influenced my emotional wellbeing and ultimately affected my skills as a caregiver. As caregivers, we are susceptible to depression and anxiety. Believe it or not, some of the foods we take into our body can exacerbate these moods.

I have good news and I have bad news. The bad news is that anxiety, lack of proper sleep, depression, and high levels of stress are common among caregivers and make it difficult for us to the best caregivers we can be. The good news is that you can do something by starting with adjustments in your diet. Now I am not going to tell you to fill every plate you have with veggies, stop eating bread, and cut out all sweets. Everyone deserves a little pleasure now and then. But what I will tell you is that some foods you would never expect can help in the alleviating some of these negative emotional effects.

So, ramp up on your eggs, dark leafy greens, pumpkins seeds, and dark chocolate (yes, I said chocolate!) to help lower your stress levels, (Aubrey, 2014) and grab your favorite fishes (I know it's "fish" but I like how the Bible refers to them as "fishes") to help battle depression (Simon Evans, n.d.). Think about what you put in your body and don't forget to drink plenty of water (Pross 2014)! Foods like whole grains, walnuts and food high in Vitamin C such as oranges, strawberries, broccoli, spinach and peppers are great foods to help cut down stress eating.

Heal Your Spirit

Caring for the total package that we call "you" requires not just taking care of your mind and your body but your spirit as well. Whether you are a deeply religious person or not, your spirit requires just as much attention as the other two components. Do not take this lightly. Staying motivated, being encouraged, and maintaining a positive attitude is essential for not just you, but necessary for the daily interaction you have with your loved one.

In my opinion, as caregiver your spirit (or soul) takes the heaviest hit in this job. It is hard to see your loved one hurting, struggling, and fighting through their health issue. For some you have the benefit of knowing that their health issue will get better over time. For others, it might be that you will be caregiving until they leave this world. Either way, your spirit will be almost as exhausted as your body. The important thing to know is that, just like your body, there are ways to strengthen your spirit. You can do a variety of things like meditate (add some yoga to this and you are killing two birds with one stone!) or read daily affirmations. And of course, there is always church.

Church, no matter what religion or denomination you are in, has served to strengthen the spirits of Black people through some of the toughest times in our lives. For some people merely being in the sanctuary of God is enough to give a person the strength to go on. I am not suggesting that everyone go to church. Spirituality is so much more than that. But I am suggesting that you connect with whatever it is that you feel will center you. And where possible, do it in a community setting where you can draw on the strength of others.

When I was caring for my mother, there were plenty of times when I felt that I was surrounded by chaos. That everywhere I turned there was some sort of drama and a lot of times I just felt like I just couldn't think straight. My solution: I would pick a day. Any day. And I would wake up in the morning, not turn on the television or the radio. I would get washed and dressed in silence. I would then go for a walk. During my walk, I would listen. I would listen to the trees blowing and the wind. Listen to the cars driving by. I would listen to my own heartbeat and the sound of my own breathing. There is a quote that I have always believed to be true. It says, "Make time for the quiet moments, as God whispers and the world is loud." During my walk, while I was silent, I listened for God's voice. In those moments, I found clarity of thought and with that clarity came a bit more strength. My mom used to say the only way you can hear God speaking is by being quiet. I learned a long time ago that quiet heals my spirit. Find out what heals yours.

I know that this chapter is to help you navigate through your emotional ups and downs and to give you tips on how balance them but I would remiss as a retired caregiver if I didn't mention the emotional rollercoaster your loved one could be going through as well. Please understand, it is important to care for yourself (care for the caregiver is essential!) but remember in chapter one when I told you that being a caregiver requires you to think differently? Well listen, if you are dealing with emotional ups and downs then you have to know that your loved one is going through some things of their own, right?

Right! So make sure that as a caregiver, while you are looking at ways to heal your body, mind and soul, that you are making sure that you are also finding ways to help your loved one do the same. After all, you are a team.

Laugh More

There is one thing that you can do that has a positive effect on you spiritually, emotional and physically and that's laugh. Now when I say you need to laugh more, I don't mean that silly crazy laugh like the Joker where people can't tell if you are being crazy or not. What I mean is that as a caregiver, life is tough and often very, very serious.

Laughter (and humor) are great ways to lighten the moment and the current situation. Ever wonder why it feels so good to have one of those deep, gut laughs? It is actually helping to heal you. There are physical health benefits (like boosting your immune system), mental health benefits (like relieving stress), and social benefits (like enhancing teamwork). (Robinson, Smith, M.A., & Segal, Ph.D., 2016) So, when people say "Laughter is the best medicine, they weren't joking.

Laughter was a huge help to me and my family when dealing with MS and my brother was the best at using laughter to help distract my mother from her pain. Often times he would make her laugh so hard that at some point, you couldn't hear her at all because she was laughing so hard. Which of course, gave him more things to tease her about. Every once in a while, I would get in on the humor by doing small things like directing her to where her coffee was by telling her it was to her left, she would reach right and then I would say, "No, Mom. Your other left." This always made her laugh. My mother was a bit of a comedian herself and would often do things like take the menu from the waitress when we would go out to pretend like she could see it. Her hearing was intensely good but her eyesight was gone but this didn't deter her from being like everyone else at the table. She would erupt in laughter when I would say, "Mom, you might want to turn that menu right-side-up so the waitress doesn't catch you!" There was certainly plenty to cry about but we made sure that we all took the time to laugh and I am so glad that we did.

Part

8 BROTHER, WHERE ART THOU?

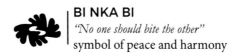

BI NKA BI
"No one should bite the other"
symbol of peace and harmony

A few years ago, a very dear friend of mine and I were talking about our caregiver journeys. Although my journey was over, his was in full swing and we often found ourselves in rather philosophical conversations about why it is that, in situations where we needed people the most, no one ever seemed to be around. Being a caregiver can be isolating. Caregivers sometimes struggle to speak to this issue and may feel guilty for needing more help than they receive. In my caregiving years, I was surrounded by people with "good intentions", however, when I needed them, they were nowhere to be found. It's easy to make promises. It's hard to follow through.

People are human. Whether they are your relatives, friends, or coworkers, you need to remember that as human beings, they will make mistakes. And they will do it quite often! Also, you need to remember that people don't always know what to say. A boyfriend once said to me, "I don't understand why you have to go to your mother's house this Sunday. Didn't you just go over there last Sunday?" At the time, I thought he was asking this because he was frustrated at the fact that he couldn't spend more time with me. In hind sight, his questions spoke to his lack of understanding of my caregiver role. He did not understand that it was important for me to be present often so that people understood my mother had an advocate and that if anything went wrong, they would have to deal with me.

I spent most of my early caregiving time feeling isolated. Some of it was voluntary as I found it was not productive to have negative people around me and my mother while we were in a battle with her MS. Negativity took too much energy, and with MS, energy was at a premium. I knew that for both my mother and I had to stay motivated, there were just some people were we going to have to let go. It wasn't out of anger or anything like that, believe me. We just needed to have focus and clarity and we needed people around us who were going to be our cheerleaders.

Unfortunately, there was also plenty of involuntary isolation. This,

I think was harder on my mother than most people realized. These were the people who just suddenly stopped calling or stopped visiting out of the blue. Disability can scare people off. They abandon old friends and loved ones, and my mother and I experienced this too. As a caregiver, you may lose some people. Not only that, but you need to be prepared to answer questions your loved one may ask when they haven't heard from so-and-so or why don't they see so-and-so. It is very easy to get angry and have hurt feelings toward the people that leave your life while you are caregiving. Especially if they were once very close to you. But as I said earlier, people are human. They often act out of fear and anxiety, not out of willful cruelty. They might not know how to help you. They might be reminded of another person they knew that had the same disability. Maybe they fear hospitals, or don't know how to interact with a sick person. They may all sound like excuses to you but for these people, it is very real.

I am reminded of my mother's very dear and close friend. She was direct in her approach. When I asked her when she would she be able to come up and see my mother, she very compassionately told me that she didn't think she would be able to and she explained to me in the most heartfelt way that it was hard for her to see my mother in a wheelchair and not up and moving around like she used to. I had so much respect for my mother's friend just because she cared enough to let me know that the reason for her departure had nothing to do with her not loving us but had more to do with her own issues.

Earlier in this book I told you that you would be surprised at the strength that you get from people when you least expect it. For every two or three people that you lose, there is always one special person who will step in just when you need the support the most. I know this because it happened to me several times, and I have heard stories from several other caregivers about the one special person in their lives who always stepped in at just the right moment.

In middle school, I was selected to participate in the NAACP ACT-

SO competition. It was an honor to be selected, and I got to represent the state of New Jersey. Yet I had to care for my mother. As the competition drew nearer, it became more evident that I wasn't going to be able to go because I just couldn't leave my mother without my help. I finally told the NAACP representative that I wouldn't be able to go because I was the primary caregiver to my mother. She said, "Before you decline to go, let me see what I can do." The next week she surprised me and told me that they had hired a home health aide to stay with my mother while I was away, and that it wouldn't cost me anything.

I might not have ever had that opportunity had I not taken a leap of faith and shared my situation. Sometimes, we choose not to let people know the challenges we face because we think that people will look at us differently or that they will pity us or even worse, that they just won't care. It is a very vulnerable position for us to be in to ask for help, but how will we ever know who will help us if we never ask? Of course, asking means they might say no or flake out. But it's not always about you. It's about getting what you need to take care of your loved one the best way you can. Sacrifice. Caregiving is all about love and sacrifice.

You are probably saying to yourself, "Well, this advice is all well and good if you're talking about friends, coworkers and classmates, etc. But what about family? You can't just drop your family, can you?" While it is true that you can't choose your family members, you can certainly choose the family members with whom you spend the most time. You love your family, right? But there are a few family members whom you are close to, and a few that you wish would get lost on the way to the family reunion simply because they drive you nuts.

Because you can't choose your family members, there will be times when making them understand what you are going through and what you need can be tough. If you are dealing with supportive family members, they will try to do their best to help you in any way they can but let's be honest, more often than not, we have the family members that are not as supportive as well would like for them to be. I am trying to be nice about it but some family members can be downright mean and use every opportunity to add to your stress. And when you snap at them because you've had limited sleep or had your loved one treat you like their emotional punching bag all day, that same inconsiderate family member will look at you like you're being "sensitive". I would use an expletive here but my mother taught me to use kind words so I will move on!

Family is family nonetheless so do your best to find the one family member that is always supportive. The one that remembers everyone's birthday, slips a couple of bucks in the hands of the young family members, and tends to be the most spiritually grounded. Take the time to talk to the supportive family members about what is going on with you and give them an opportunity to step up to the plate and help you out with a few things.

When I say share what is going on and what you need from your family, that doesn't mean everyone in your family! Everyone in your family isn't going to be able to —or even want to —help you emotionally or financially. Stay away from the family members who like to spread negativity and gossip. Stay particularly far away from the relatives and family members who overshare on social media. Family isn't perfect, but if there are loving people in your family, stay connected to them. If you didn't win the family lottery, it's time to find friends whom you can make into your family of choice.

One final note – if you are a person that has some religious conviction, be sure that you stay connected to the prayer warriors in your life. The folks that still pray for others before themselves and always, always have a word of strength for you even if you didn't ask them to provide one. The folks that are in tune with your spirit and call you just when you need it most. When you are asleep, they are praying for your strength, your happiness, and the loved one you are caring for. They are asking God to help you with guidance and patience. You may not know a lot of them, but I can guarantee that you know at least one or two of them. The next time you see them, hug them and say, "Thank you," because when you are in your toughest hour, they are calling in a favor from God to help you to get through another day. Sometimes that is all they can give, but sometimes that is just what you need.

Part

9 REST FOR THE WEARY

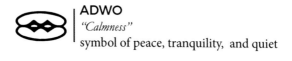

ADWO

"Calmness"

symbol of peace, tranquility, and quiet

You're tired, aren't you? Be honest. I know you're tired. Tired of fighting with health insurance companies. Tired of dealing with social workers, home health aides, and insensitive people. Tired of having to explain why you're so tired, right? I know. I was in your shoes once. I know that rest for a caregiver is a luxury that we just don't seem to have very often. Caregivers may do everything for others, but they're terrible at caring for themselves. I didn't take my first real vacation until after my mother passed away because I used vacation time to take my mother to her doctor visits. At times when I did manage to get out of town, I spent so much time worrying about whether my mother would be alright while I was away; it just never felt like I got a chance to relax.

I was the worst when it came to care for myself, which is why this chapter was so hard for me even thirteen years after my mother's passing. I hope you will learn from my mistakes.

One of the things that made it difficult for me to take care of myself as well as my mother was that I convinced myself that if I was taking care of myself, I was taking time and effort away from my mother. It seemed so selfish to me to make time to rest when my mother needed me so much. If you have been a caregiver for a long time, you are probably shaking your head up and down as you read my distorted logic. Well you can stop agreeing now. Not caring for the caregiver and putting your own mental and physical health aside is a sure-fire way to burn yourself out. It does not help you or your loved one in the long run. When you don't take good care of yourself, you also cannot take good care of your loved one.

I know you're thinking that there isn't ever enough time in the day to do all the things you need to do for your loved one--let alone work, school, family, friends, or the endless stream of other obligations life throws your way. The job of a caregiver is never done. You are never going to get less schoolwork. Work is always going to make projects for you. Your children and/or spouse are always going to need you.

So, if you are going to be pulled into a million different directions each day, why not let caring for yourself be another part of your juggling act? The fact of the matter is you are no good to anyone if you are irritable, tired, sick, worn out, and unhealthy. The funny thing is that we say to ourselves all the time, "Nothing will get done unless we do it". If that's the case, why is it that it is so hard for us to take care of ourselves? It could be a variety of things: guilt, obligation, etc.

It is a common mistake that a lot of new and perhaps even some more seasoned caregivers make by assuming that their own health and wellbeing are not as important as the person for whom they are caring for. But what happens when your loved one gets rushed to the hospital and you can't go meet them there and give them support or even make sure that the hospital has all the information they need because you have been fighting a cold that just hasn't gone away for weeks? And what would your loved one want for you? They want you to be happy and healthy.

I decided to poke fun at myself a little bit just to show you how unbelievably stubborn I was while I was a caregiver. And believe me, I was pretty stubborn! I was bad at taking care of myself and so I am going to tell you five excuses that not only I, but other caregivers have used as reasons to not take care of ourselves. If you have used any of these excuses yourself, shame on you

Excuse #1 – "I Don't Have Enough Time to Relax"

For some reason, we have been led to believe that eventually, there will be a point in our daily lives that we will have time to do all the things we need to do. Not so, my friend. There will always be bills to pay, projects at work, children to attend to, and a million other things. If you wait until there is enough time, you will be waiting forever! The idea here is to make time not wait for time. Just like you make time to help a friend in need or make time for things your boss may ask you for at the last minute at work, please figure out a way to squeeze a little time in for yourself. Even if it's only for twenty or thirty minutes. That might not seem like much time but try it, you would be amazed at how much it helps to just have a little "you time."

I eventually learned how to make a little time for myself by going to the nail salon every two weeks and getting a manicure and pedicure. At the nail salon, I was able to relax in the massage chair and allow someone to take care of me for a little while. Sometimes, I would even fall asleep not realizing that I was worn out. At the end of my appointment, I felt refreshed, a little less stressed, and on top of that I had my nails and toes looking fabulous!

Excuse #2 – "No One Knows How to Do What I Do"

I have to admit, sadly, that this excuse was the one I used the most. It sounds a bit arrogant; wouldn't you say? The fact of the matter is, I really believed that there was no one that could care for my mother as well as I could. I managed to have everything scheduled – meals, doctor visits, hair and nail appointments, everything! It never occurred to me that if I would have allowed people to work with me then there might have been a few people who could have done all the things I did. But like many caregivers do, I lacked trust in others and ended up putting way too much pressure on myself. That kind of pressure will eventually put wear and tear on you so, please don't use my excuse as a reason to not take out time for yourself. You cannot control every aspect of your loved one's care. There is going to be a point where you will have to ask others for help and then ultimately let them do it. Once you let others help, you will realize that you are not the only one that can do the job. Granted, no one will love your loved one like you do but believe me, with the right instruction, you can delegate some responsibilities to others you trust so that you can take a few minutes to breathe!

Excuse #3 — "What If Something Happens?"

A friend of mine once said that there is no way to stop the inevitable. That if something was meant to happen, it will. I am not necessarily sure I agree with her but I do know that this "helplessness" is very frustrating for caregivers. The idea that there is something we can't control. We try, as caregivers to think of every scenario that could happen, and we try to make sure we put things in place to make sure nothing does happen but ultimately, we have this feeling that we can't really go anywhere or do anything because we feel we need to be there just in case something does happen. It is a vicious cycle and one that is very hard to break. My advice for this is simple. There is no crystal ball that will allow you to see what is going to happen when you are away. All you can do is be as organized as you can be and as flexible as you can be. If you have all your bases covered for a vacation or even just to get away for a few hours and something happens, just know that it didn't happen because you took time for yourself. No one is going to punish you for trying to recharge.

Excuse #4 — "I'm Fine. I Don't Need Time Away."

This is a good one, and an excuse that one of my college friends uses all the time. I am not quite sure where we caregivers got the "we are invincible" gene, but somehow, we all have it. Being a caregiver doesn't mean that we now have a big "S" on our chests and that we are not allowed to feel tired, weak, or worn out. When we feel these things, it simply means we are human. One thing I have learned from using this excuse is that if you tell people you are fine, they will believe you! Say it often enough and people will stop asking you if you need help. Then you'll be sitting around one day wondering why it is that no one is around to help. My suggestion: Don't say it if you don't mean it. There is nothing wrong with saying, "I need a little help here, people!" No one is a mind reader so if you need help, ask for it!

Excuse #5 — "There is Too Much to Do."

This one goes together with Excuse #1. Yes, there is a lot to do. But guess what? It is going to be there whether you take some time out for yourself or not. So, why don't you sit down for a half an hour and have that cup of tea before you start running around for the rest of the day? It will make all the difference in the world.

Part

10 FORCED "RETIREMENT"

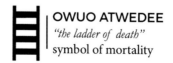

OWUO ATWEDEE
"the ladder of death"
symbol of mortality

This part of the caregiver guide was by far the most difficult one to write. If some of you are lucky enough to have been a caregiver to someone that only needed you temporarily because they were able to get better, then you are truly blessed. For those of you, however, who have lost their loved one due to a disability or ailment, this chapter will be tough to read but we will get through it together.

As of September 2006, I became retired a caregiver. Not because it is a cool title to have, but because that is exactly what it feels like. In the corporate world when a person retires, it means they have put their heart and soul into a job or organization for a very long time and now the time has ended. There may be retirement parties and plans for the future. Their hard work has left a positive mark on themselves, those around them, and hopefully the organization itself. Retiring as a caregiver is a little different. There's no party. You may even wonder if the work you've done matters. I'm here to tell you that it does and that it did.

Being a retired caregiver comes with a sense of both accomplishment and loss. When my mother passed away, I spend so many days and nights trying to figure out what regular people did on a daily basis. For over 20 years, my days had been filled with doctor visits, running double the number of errands, paying double the number of bills, arguing with home health aides, physical therapy schedules, and so much more. But once you retire, all you hear and feel is silence. Silence in a way you have never experienced it before.

Some people feel empty. Emptiness, however, implies you have given all and have nothing left to give. You will always feel like there is more you could have done. I certainly did. If my mom was still with me and needed me, I still had more support, more reserves more love to give. That's the nature of unconditional love. There's always more. But she wasn't with me anymore, and there was…silence.

Being retired is no fun. I mean, you spend all this time and energy learning so much stuff. You learn to understand your loved one's needs, thoughts, aches and pains. You prayed for strength on the tough days, got it back, depleted it, and prayed again. You fought with relatives and friends when they were insensitive. You wore so many hats--therapist, confidant, enforcer, and now all of that is gone. You had gotten so good at being all things for your loved one that now it is hard to separate you, the caregiver, and you the individual.

Like I said, this chapter was the toughest to write because even thirteen years from the date of my mother's passing, I am still trying to find me. The role of caregiver had become so ingrained in me that trying to separate it from my personality was and continues to be nearly impossible. The week after my mother died, I had to go to a department store to buy a new suit for work. Simple task, right? I thought so too, until I went into the dressing room to try the suit on and all of a sudden, I felt an overwhelming wave of sadness. I began weeping, much to the dismay of the poor department store employee who tried to console me and had no idea what was wrong. After about five minutes or so, I got myself together, put the suit back on the rack and walked out of the store.

In that moment I realized that for most of my life, I had never bought anything for just me. When I used to buy clothes for me, I would always buy clothes for my mom. If I paid bills for me, her bills got paid too. Even when I got my hair and nails done, rest assured I made an appointment for my mom too. So, when I was about to buy one suit for myself, it hit me like a ton of bricks. I was no longer a caregiver. My mom was gone. I was alone. Silence.

Peeling yourself away from your caregiver way of life is like taking off an old Band-Aid. You get so used to having the Band-Aid there that when it comes off, it hurts a little and although the sensitive area it was covering is staring to heal, it is not used to being exposed. It is raw and will take some time to strengthen in the elements to eventually become as strong and visibly the same as the skin around it. In an earlier chapter I explained the necessity of taking care of yourself as a caregiver. Now you must begin to care for yourself as a retired caregiver.

The good news is that you already have the tools you need to be a retired caregiver. You don't have to learn anything new. You just have to redirect your care for your loved one to yourself. Remember when you were first starting out as a caregiver and you had to learn all this stuff about the health care profession, learn to keep important documents together and document doctor visits, check-ups and things like that? Well, now you get to take care of YOU. All that organization, energy, time can now be put into you. Trust me, none of the skills you learned previously are going to go to waste! You've built up an immense reserve of strength. And now you don't have to spend that strength fighting a painful battle on behalf of the person you love.

There are two things I do want to warn you about as a retired caregiver. The first thing is to be very wary of trying to fill the void. Besides the tremendous sense of loss when you lose a loved one, there is this need to be useful. It is very powerful and so sometimes retired caregivers like me will inadvertently pour ourselves into people or things that we shouldn't. We do this to feel useful and to fill that void. Do not do this! Take some time to think about what really deserves your time and attention. Think about how you can use the extra time to improve, support, and love yourself. Remember, it is not selfish of you to do this. It is something you need to do.

When my mother passed away, my brother told me something very wise that I will share with you. He asked me, "So, what are you going to do with all your free time now?" I hadn't thought about it and then he said, "Well, whatever it is, make sure that it is something that is worth your time." I am very glad I took his advice and used the time to write. Writing this book and trying to offer support and information that would help you, the reader of this book, was definitely worth my time.

The second thing is to not allow people to pull you out of retirement for their own personal gain. Most people you know will have seen what kind of work you put into caring for your loved one, and will either try to get you assist them in their own caregiving or try to get you to step in as caregiver for someone they love because they are too scared or feel they are not equipped to be caregivers themselves. Do not fall for this! I am not saying that you can't offer suggestions or give advice. I just want to let you know that as a retired caregiver, you now have skills that everyone will want and need. You can be their resource, but you cannot do their work or their learning for them.

Well, retired caregiver, the road you were on was long. Now it is time to redirect your attention to you. I will be honest and tell you it is difficult, but you can do it. I know that you can. Be proud of the work that you put into caring for your loved one and begin the journey of taking care of you. I will tell you what the first step is…

…breathe.

References

Aubrey, A. (2014, July 14). NPR. Retrieved from www.npr.org:http://www.npr.org/sections/thesalt/2014/07/14/329529110/food-mood-connection-how-you-eat-can-amp-up-or-tamp-down-stress

Centers for Disease Control and Prevention. (2015, December 22). Centers for Disease Control and Prevention. Retrieved from Centers for Disease Control and Prevention: https://www.cdc.gov/tuskegee/timeline.htm

Donald Venes, M. (2013). Taber's Cyclopedic Medical Dictionary. F.A. Davis Company.

National Multiple Sclerosis Society, (. (2018, June). https://www.nationalmssociety.org/What-is-MS/Who-Gets-MS/African-American-Resources. Retrieved from www.nationalmssociety.org: http://www.nationalmssociety.org/NationalMSSociety/media/MSNationalFiles/Brochures/Brochure-African-Americans-and-Multiple-Sclerosis.pdf

Pross N, Demazières A, Girard N, Barnouin R, Metzger D, Klein A, et al. (2014) Effects of Changes in Water Intake on Mood of High and Low Drinkers. PLoS ONE 9(4): e94754. doi:10.1371/journal.pone.0094754

Roberts Kennedy, PhD, APRN, BC, B., Clomus Mathis, PhD, C., & Woods, MSN, A. K. (2007). African Americans and Their Distrust of the Healthcare System: Healthcare for Diverse Populations. Journal of Cultural Diversity, 56-60.

Robinson, L., Smith, M.A., M., & Segal, Ph.D., J. (2016, November 1). Help Guide. Retrieved from HelpGuide.org: http://www.helpguide.org/articles/emotional-health/laughter-is-the-best-medicine.htm

Simon Evans, P. (n.d.). University of Michigan Depression Center. Retrieved from www.depressiontoolkit.org: http://www. depressiontoolkit.org/news/omega3_and_brain_health.asp

Sloot, R. (2010). The Immortal Life of Henrietta Lacks. New York: Crown Publishers.

Weinstein, S. (2018, February 8). Care for Your Mind. Retrieved November 2018, from http://careforyourmind.org/stigma-and-other-factors-affect-blacks-use-of-mental-health-services/

About the Author

Ky'a Jackson was a caregiver for over 20 years before becoming an author. She received her bachelor's degree from the first Black institute of higher learning - Cheyney University of Pennsylvania and her master's degree from Temple University. Her family hails from Camden, New Jersey and she currently resides in Philadelphia, Pennsylvania. *The Color of Care* is her first book.

Made in the
USA
Lexington, KY